JAZZ CLUB

Clarinet
Grades 1-2

Piano Accompaniment
Contents

Series Editor: Sadie Cook

Production Editor: Anna Joyce

Music Engraving & CD Production: Artemis Music Limited

Recorded by: Jeff Leach (piano)

Cover Design: Dominic Brookman

Published 2001

All titles © 2001 International Music Publications Limited

Clarinet
Grades 1-2

JAZZ CLUB

IMP

International
MUSIC
Publications

© International Music Publications Limited
Griffin House 161 Hammersmith Road London W6 8BS England

Introduction

Welcome to **Jazz Club**

This book contains ten pieces (two unaccompanied) that have been written to reflect the diverse **jazz** styles used by professional **jazz** musicians over the past fifty years or so. Each piece has been written specifically for the **clarinet** making best use of the range, **timbre** and agility of the instrument. The pieces become gradually more difficult as you make your way through the book. A short paragraph outlining tips on **rhythm, swing and articulation** for each piece is included in the instrumental insert, together with a listening recommendation.

In this first book, the difficulty lies mostly with interpreting **jazz rhythms, ties, pushed beats, swing** etc, however the range of notes required should present few problems. The accompaniments are designed to provide a strong rhythmic and harmonic background and although at first some may look a little tricky, a pianist of modest ability will find them playable with a small amount of practice.

Virtually every **jazz** musician has developed individuality of style by listening to other musicians and their recordings. It is strongly recommended that any **jazz** study-programme should include listening to **jazz** recordings – in particular compare the tones achieved by different performers and the way they apply varying degrees of **swing**.

Enjoy this book and let it be the start of a lifelong affinity with **jazz**.

Jazz Music
for Beetles

Tall trees

Slowly, with expression

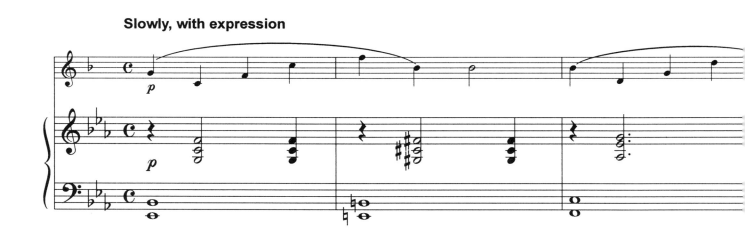

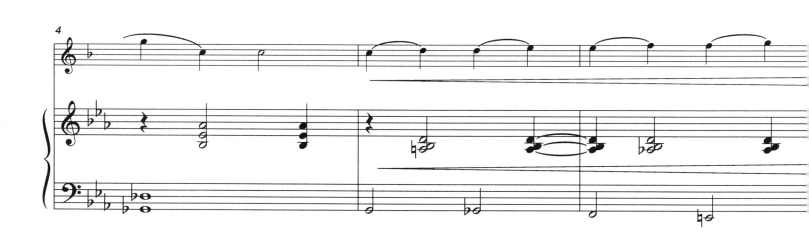

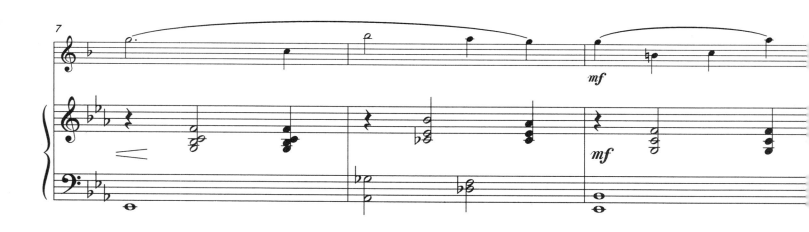

Gloomy jack

Fairly fast

Chilli pepper

Bad hair day

The Hungry blues

Nestor leaps in

COCKTAIL shaker